this
book
belongs to

HUMZA
Humza
Ahmed

First published in the United Kingdom in 1428[AH] (2007[CE]) by
Learning Roots
PO Box 51433
London
N17 6QR
www.learningroots.com

Acknowledgements
The publisher thanks Allah, Lord of the Worlds, for making this publication possible.

British Library Cataloguing in Publication Data
A CIP catalogue record for this book is available from the British Library.

Printed and bound in China

ISBN: 978-1-905516-19-3

STEM
SERIES

Ages 6-7

Stories of the
Prophets
قصص الأنبياء

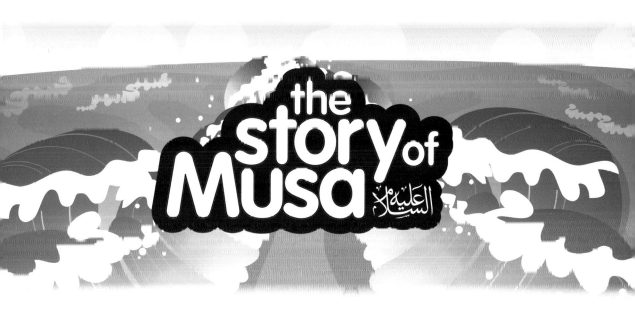

the
story of
Musa العليه السلام

Learning Roots

While the incorporation of

professional curriculum design standards,

hallmark literacy & numeracy conventions,

modern learning theory

and comprehensive coverage of the Islamic Sciences

all serve to make the Stem Series a

feature-rich, pioneering and unparalleled resource;

the real secret of the series lies in it's creative approach

in both content and design

that engage, enthuse and enliven

children's study and love of the Islamic Sciences.

contents

You are on a journey.

You will learn about the lives of some of the best men that ever lived.

These were men sent by Allah

You will learn why they were sent,

who they were sent to,

and what lessons we can learn from their lives.

They are the Prophets.

The first of them is Adam ﷵ

and the last of them is Muhammad ﷺ.

setting off

As with any journey, you will need to know where you are going; having a map of your route certainly helps! On the following pages you will see a map of the Prophets mentioned in the Noble Quran. Follow the path on the map carefully and look out for the names you have heard before.

From amongst all of these Prophets of Allah, five are mentioned in the Quran (in Surah Al-Ahzaab, Ash-Shura & Al-Ahqaaf) as أولوا العزم or Prophets of great determination. They are Nuh عليه السلام, Ibrahim عليه السلام, Musa عليه السلام, Eesa عليه السلام and Muhammad ﷺ. We shall learn about the life of Muhammad ﷺ in detail in a dedicated subject in the Stem Series. For now, we'll take a closer look at the other four Prophets mentioned, as well as the Prophet Adam عليه السلام; the first Prophet of Allah. Take a look at the map on the next page...

Eesa عليه السلام

Ibrahim عليه السلام

Musa عليه السلام

As you may have guessed from the title of this book, you'll be learning about the story of Musa ﷺ. You can discover more about the other Prophets in the rest of this series.

As you travel, you will need to acquaint yourself with some essential information. Without it, you will be lost, and may not reach your final destination. Read up on the following symbols to find out what to expect along your way.

Before you begin any journey, you need to know where you are going and why you are going there. With all the stories in this book, your aim is broken into three parts. You **must** be able to read the story yourself, summarize the main events and place them in the correct order. You **should** be able to understand the finer details of what occurred in the story. Finally, you **could** be able to understand the reasoning behind some of the story events. You will be able to test whether you have achieved your targets at the end of each section by attempting to overcome the obstacles in your way.

One of the other things you need to do before any journey is to prepare! **Pack Your Bags** involves reminding yourself about the meanings of some essential key words that occur in the story.

*Once you have set off on your journey, you'll need to think actively about what you are learning. **Reflections** occur in the middle of stories and get you to ponder a little deeper into the events.*

Once the reading is over, you'll take a well earned rest at the Rest Point. You'll do some light amusement to ensure you understand the language used in the story.

*Now begins your chance to prove what you have learnt. You have to cross three different obstacles, each getting harder as you go along. By completing each of these you will ensure you have covered the aims of your journey. First you have to **Jump the Fence** by proving you know enough about the events of the story.*

*The next task is a little harder. **Cross the River** is all about checking whether you picked up the smaller details of what actually happened in the story.*

*The final and hardest task is called **Climb the Mountain.** Here you have to show an understanding of why things happened the way they did in the story.*

*After completing each section, be sure to have your answers marked in **The Farewell Mark** chapter at the end of this book. Well that's all you need to know before you start! It's time to begin your journey. Bismillah! Here's a little introduction for you...*

Shaytaan was still out there making his call. He played his trick on a king called Fir'own. He thought he was god and never prayed to Allah. Fir'own had a powerful army and used it to harm his people. Something had to be done to stop him...

the magic trick

Before you begin your journey, you'll need to be prepared. Some of the
words that occur in the story are mentioned below. Take a quick look
at them to see which ones you already know. We'll do some work on
these and other words at the end of the story!

HEAVENS

MESSENGER

MAGICIAN

STRIKING

SLITHERING

Allah sent the Prophet Musa *'Alay-his-salaam* to Fir'own. Musa entered his palace. Fir'own waited with all of his men around him in pride.

"I am the Messenger of the Lord of the worlds," said Musa without any fear.

"Who is the Lord of the worlds?" asked Fir'own. He did not seem to understand.

"The Lord of the Heavens and the Earth," said Musa.

Fir'own turned to his men. "Did you hear that?" he said. "The Messenger sent to you is mad!" Fir'own tried to make fun of Musa, but it didn't work.

"He is your Lord and the Lord of your fathers,"
said Musa. "He is the Lord of the East and
the West."

Fir'own did not know what to say. Musa told
him the truth in such a clear way.

"If you take any god other than me," said
Fir'own, "then I will throw you in prison!"
Fir'own tried to show his power.

"What if I can prove it to you?" asked Musa.

"Show it then, if you are telling the truth,"
replied Fir'own.

Musa threw his stick. It turned into a snake, alive and moving. Then Musa drew out his hand from his pocket. It was shining and glowing white for all to see.

Subhaanallah! Such clear signs and proofs from Allah! But Fir own had such a hard heart that he still did not believe. What do you think he will accuse Musa ﷺ of next in order to carry on with his evil ways? Write your thoughts down below and continue reading to see if you are correct.

He was trying to prove that he was a prophet.

Fir'own was shocked. "Have you come to drive us out of our land with your magic?" he asked. "We will show you our magic too!"

Fir'own called his best magicians from every land. People gathered at high noon to see the show.

The magicians came with sticks in their hands. "Will you throw first, or shall we?" they asked.

"You throw first," replied Musa. The magicians threw their sticks and played a magic trick. The sticks turned into snakes, slithering from here to there. The people were struck with fear.

"Do not fear," said Allah to Musa, "throw what is in your right hand." Musa threw his stick.

It turned into a real snake, eating all the other snakes there. It was a miracle from Allah. The magicians knew it too.

"We believe in the Lord of Musa," they said.

"How dare you believe in Him before I allow you!" said Fir'own with rage.

It was too late. The magicians followed the truth, but Fir'own never changed his ways. Strange things started happening to him and his people...

Their rivers dried out. They had no fruits to enjoy. Then water flooded their land. Armies of locusts, lice and frogs spread everywhere. They found no peace or time for rest.

These were signs from Allah so that they might believe. But they turned away every time. Fir'own had enough. He was now planning to kill Musa.

Rest Point

Well, it's quite an exciting story up until now, wouldn't you say? Will Fir'own ever learn? Before we continue, lets do a little word-work. Write each of the words below in a sentence that shows it's meaning.

heavens

Allah created the heuvens.

prison

prison is Jail.

messenger

Allah has messengers

shocked

Fir'own is shocked.

magician

Musa is not a magician.

striking

The lightning strikes the pole.

slithering

The snakes slithed through the pain.

gathered

The people gathered near when its over.

noon

12:00 PM is noon.

Musa

Musa is a prophet.

Fir'own

Fir'own is a king.

shining

The Sun is shining bright.

31

Jump the Fence

Put the events in the order that they occurred in the story. Then write their letters in order in the circles below. You will have to think of the missing event yourself. What word do the letters in the circles spell?

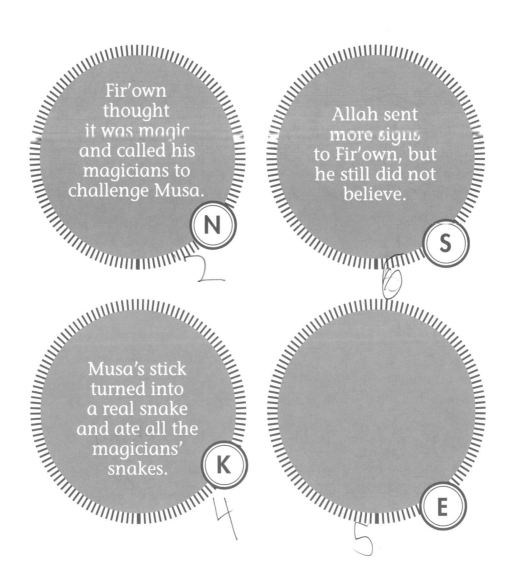

Fir'own thought it was magic and called his magicians to challenge Musa.

N

2

Allah sent more signs to Fir'own, but he still did not believe.

S

6

Musa's stick turned into a real snake and ate all the magicians' snakes.

K

4

E

5

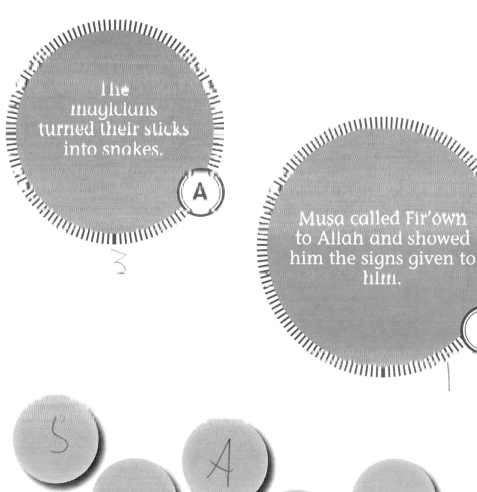

The magicians turned their sticks into snakes.

A

3

Musa called Fir'own to Allah and showed him the signs given to him.

S

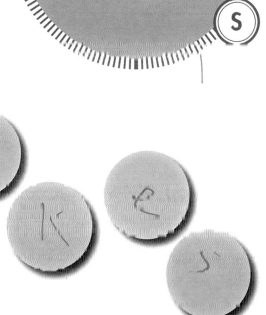

S N A K E S

Cross the River

What a wavy mess! Cross this wild river by connecting questions to their answers using wavy lines. It's a bit of a maze!

Who was with Fir'own when Musa went to meet him?

Musa

Kill him

What proofs did Musa show Fir'own?

Which Prophet was sent to Fir'own?

In his palace

What did Fir'own think Musa was trying to do?

What did Fir'own decide to do after Musa showed him his proofs?

Musa told Fir'own about Allah.

The magicians

How did the magicians turn their sticks into snakes?

Turning his stick into a snake and making his hand shining white

What started happening to Fir'own and his people?

Where did Musa go to meet Fir'own?

What did Allah tell Musa not to do?

What did Fir'own want to do to Musa?

Who threw their sticks first?

What did Musa tell Fir'own?

What did Musa's snake do to the other snakes?

Ate them all up.

his magicians to challenge Musa.

Drive him out of his town.

Climb the Mountain

Just one more obstacle to go before we can continue with the story. All of the statements below are incorrect. Correct each statement and rewrite them in the spaces provided.

1 You can tell that Fir'own was making fun of Musa because he was being nice to him.

mean

2 Fir'own tried to show his power by threatening to throw himself in prison.

musa

3 The magicians became Muslims because they were scared of Fir'own.

believed in god

4 Fir'own was angry with the magicians because their tricks did not work.

believed in allah

5 Strange things started to happen to Fir'own and his people because they lost the challenge between Musa and the magicians.

disbelieved in Allah's message.

the splitting sea

So it's finally time to find out how this story ends. Before you begin,
have a quick look at the words below to see which of them you already
know. We'll do some work on these and other words at the end.

HOPE

CRUSHING

Allah told Musa to gather the Muslims and leave the city. They left under the cover of darkness in the night.

Fir'own found out in the early morning and called his army together. He began his chase in anger at sunrise.

Musa and the Muslims reached a sea. It was in their way. There was nowhere to escape. Fir'own was not far behind. The Muslims were losing hope fast.

"Fir'own and his army will catch us up," they said in fear.

"No way!" said Musa. "My Lord is with me. He will guide me out." Musa never lost hope in Allah. He struck the sea with his stick. Something amazing started to happen...

Musa showed his trust in Allah at a time when others around him were losing hope. This shows a very strong part of a Muslims character. Can you think of other strong characteristics of Musa that you have come across in this story?

He trusted Allah SWT.
He was brave.
He was smart.
He was fearless

The sea started splitting into two parts. A pathway was cleared in the middle. The Muslims hurried through and reached the other side. But they were not safe yet.

Fir'own ran through the sea with his army, hunting the Muslims down. He thought the sea would stay split for him too. Fir'own fell into the trap.

The two sides of the sea began falling apart. They came crashing down, crushing the army in between. Fir'own's army drowned in the deep water. They were never to be seen again.

Fir'own had no army to save him now. Allah took away his palaces and his power. That day he was weaker than a fly. Fir'own found no place to hide from the punishment of Allah.

Allah raised him high on a wave for all to see. "I believe in the God that the Muslims believe in," said Fir'own just as he was about to die. But now it was too late.

The sea swallowed him in. That was the end of Fir'own. Allah saved Musa and the Muslims. Shaytaan's trick did not work on them. They followed the truth and did what Allah likes. That is our aim in life.

Rest Point

We've reached the end of this story, but there is still some work to be done. In the spaces provided below, write each word in a sentence to show it's meaning.

chase

I chased the dog.

sunrise

Sunrise came at five o.clock.

hope

I hope I have pizza.

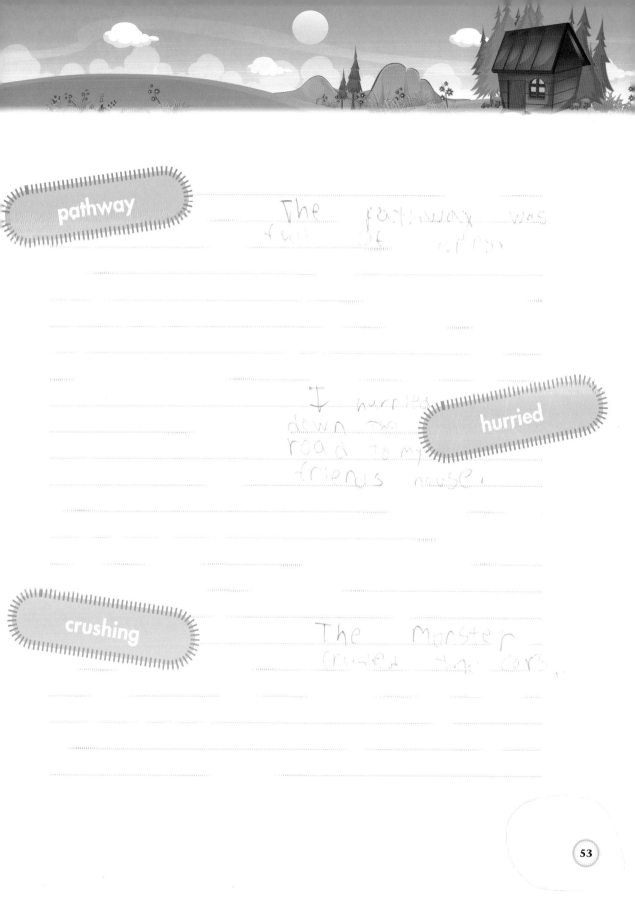

pathway

The pathway was run of the path

hurried

I hurried down the road to my friends house.

crushing

The Monster crushed the cars.

53

Jump the Fence

We'll test more of your drawing skills in this activity. Draw the two missing pictures in the sequence and describe what is happening in each of the pictures. You'll also have to number the events in the right order too!

3

There were a bunch of rocks in the way.

6

Firown people around in the water

1

They were sleeping.

(4)

Allah made a runaway

(5)

The people of Firawn crossed the sea

(7)

They escaped at night

Cross the River

We have made it easier to cross this river by giving you the answers to choose from. Write the letters of your answers in order. What word do they spell?

What did Allah tell Musa to do?

T   To kill Fir'own.

A   To stay in the city.

B   To leave the city.

L   To fight Fir'own's army.

E   To leave his people.

When did Musa leave the city?

C   At midday.

L   In the afternoon.

E   In the evening.

A   In the morning.

R   At night.

When did Fir'own find out what Musa had done?

H   At night.

O   In the morning.

P   In the afternoon.

E   In the evening.

D   At midday.

He waited for Musa to come back.

He did nothing.

(He gathered his army and chased Musa.)

He sent a spy to find out where Musa had gone.

He started to cry.

What was in Musa's way?

A mountain.

A sea.

A river.

A big rock.

A spring of water.

What happened to the sea when Musa struck it?

The sea turned into a pathway.

The sea split into three parts with two paths in the middle.

The sea changed colour.

The water in the sea disappeared.

The sea split into two parts with a path in the middle.

What did the Muslims do once the sea was split?

R	They hurried through the path and reached the other side.
I	They stayed where they were.
G	They went back to the city.
H	They swam in the sea.
T	They started to fight Fir'own and his army.

What did Fir'own do when he saw the sea split?

W	He went back to the city.
H	He followed the Muslims down the sea pathway.
A	He stayed where he was.
L	He told his army to lay down their weapons.
E	He went to sleep.

What happened to the sea as Fir'own tried to cross it?

B	The sea came together again after Fir'own reached the other side.
O	The sea came together again and Fir'own and his army drowned.
A	The ground swallowed him and his army in.
R	The sea came together again but Fir'own swam safely ashore.
D	The sea split for him as he crossed.

C "I do not want to die."

R "I believe I am God."

O "I believe in the God that the Muslims believe in."

W "I want to go back to my palace."

N "I want to kill Musa."

D He drowned in the sea and died.

E He swam safely ashore.

A He became Muslim.

L He was saved by his army.

He reached the other side of the sea.

Climb the Mountain

Write an appropriate question for each of the following answers in the spaces provided.

1. Why could Musa not continue his journey?

Cause the red sea was blocking.

2. Why were the Muslims losing hope?

they were scared.

3. How can you tell that Musa never lost hope in Allah?

musa said Alloh will guide him Out.

1. Why were the Muslims not safe even though they crossed the sea?

because firown was close behind

5. Why did the sea not stay split for Fir'own?

he was bad guy.

6. Why did Allah raise Fir'own high on a sea wave?

7. Why was it too late for Fir'own to believe?

8. Why did Shaytaan's trick not work with Musa?

the farewell mark

Every journey, no matter how long, must come to an end. You have come to the end of your journey through the life of Prophet 'Musa إلاهلا. One of the ways you can measure your success is through seeing how well you did in clearing the obstacles that came in your path. Suggested answers to each chapter are offered in the pages that follow. You are encouraged to have your progress marked.

However, there is more to measuring your success than just clearing the obstacles. One of the most valuable measures is your own thoughts on what you have learnt and enjoyed most. Hopefully, you will take away a treasure chest of lessons from this wonderful and important story, and continue learning more about it in the future. This chapter offers you the chance to judge for yourself what was your most valuable farewell mark.

At the end of a journey, it's always nice to pause and think over what you can most benefit from. Think hard about what were the most valuable lessons you learnt during this journey. Take a moment to think again and select one lesson, idea or thought that you will take away from your experience…

Did you really think it was all over?

It did not take long for Shaytaan to try again. The people kept on falling for his tricks. Allah sent many Prophets to guide them back. But instead they turned away. Something had to give way…

Discover what happens in the story of 'Eesa عليه السلام.

the magic trick

Section	Answer	Comments
	He would accuse Musa of magic.	
	Heavens: Allah created the heavens and the earth and everything in between them. **Prison:** The criminal was put into prison. **Messengers:** Allah sent many messengers to call people to Islam. **Shocked:** The people were shocked by the magic tricks. **Magician:** A magician is someone who practices magic. **Striking:** Lightening was striking all night. **Slithering:** The snake slithered from place to place. **Gathered:** The people gathered in the town centre for a meeting. **Noon:** Noon is the time that is the middle of the day. **Musa:** Musa was a prophet and messenger of Allah. **Fir'own:** Fir'own was a bad king in the time of Musa. **Shining:** The glass was shining as the sun's rays reflected off it.	*The answers offered here are by way of suggestion only. Credit should be given for any valid response.*
	Word spelt: SNAKES. **Missing event:** The magicians became Muslims.	
	Which Prophet was sent to Fir'own? **Musa.** Where did Musa go to meet Fir'own? **In his palace.** Who was with Fir'own when Musa went to meet him? **All of Fir'own's men.** What did Musa tell Fir'own? **Musa told Fir'won about Allah.** What proofs did Musa show Fir'own? **Turning his stick into a snake and making his hand shining white.** What did Fir'own think Musa was trying to do? **Drive him out of his town.** What did Fir'own decide to do after Musa showed him his proofs? **Call his magicians to challenge Musa.** Who threw their sticks first? **The magicians.** How did the magicians turn their sticks into snakes? **By a magic trick.** What did Allah tell Musa not to do? **Not to fear.** What did Musa's snake do to the other snakes? **Ate them all up.** What started happening to Fir'own and his people? **Their rivers dried out, they had no fruits, their land was flooded and insects were everywhere.** What did Fir'own want to do to Musa? **Kill him.**	
	1. Fir'own was making fun of Musa because he called him mad. **2.** Fir'own tried to show his power by threatening to throw Musa in prison. **3.** The magicians became Muslims because they realized the truth. **4.** Fir'own was angry with the magicians because they became Muslims. **5.** Strange things started to happen to Fir'own and his people so that they would believe in Allah after seeing such clear signs.	*The answers offered here are brief. Elaboration may be explored by the respondent.*

the splitting sea

Section	Answer	Comments
	Assertive and bold character, as shown in his conversation with Fir'own. Fearing no one but Allah.	
	Chase: Fir'own began his chase of the Muslims in the morning. **Sunrise:** The fajr prayer is prayed before sunrise. **Hope:** Musa had hope that Allah will help him. **Pathway:** The sea split into two making a pathway in between. **Hurried:** The Muslims hurried to reach to the other side. **Crushing:** The sea came together again, crushing the army in between.	*The answers offered here are by way of suggestion only. Credit should be given for any valid response.*
	1. Musa left the town. (Picture of town at night.) **2.** Fir'own chased him at sunrise. (Picture of army with the sun rising in the background.) **3.** The sea was blocking Musa's way and Fir'own was not far away. (Missing: Picture of a sea.) **4.** Allah split the sea for Musa. (Missing: Picture of splitting sea.) **5.** Fir'own followed the Muslims and began crossing the sea. (Picture of army running through a sea path.) **6.** Allah made the sea normal again and Fir'own and his army drowned. (Picture of drowning army.)	
	Words spelt: BROTHERHOOD	
	1. A sea was blocking his way. **2.** Fir'own's army was catching them up quickly. **3.** Musa said 'Allah will guide me out.' **4.** Fir'own's army began to chase them down the sea path. **5.** He did not have any trust in Allah. **6.** So that everyone could see him. **7.** The Angel of Death had already approached him. **8.** He followed the truth and did what Allah likes.	*The answers offered here are brief. Elaboration may be explored by the respondent.*

my rough working space